A spiritual conversation at Starbucks between three high school friends.

Greg Stier

D2S Publishing

D2S Publishing

Venti Jesus Please
Copyright © 2008 by Dare 2 Share Ministries, Inc.
All rights reserved.

A D2S Publishing book
PO Box 745323
Arvada, CO 80006

Editor: Jane Dratz
Cover design: Anthony P. Alberico

Stier, Greg.
Venti Jesus Please: A spiritual conversation at Starbucks
between three high school friends
ISBN-13: 978-0-97255-072-7
ISBN-10: 0-97255-072-0

Library of Congress Control Number: 2007935063
Printed in the United States of America

1

We only had an hour and a half before the high school musical was scheduled to start. So instead of going home, we decided to head to Starbucks and get some liquid refreshment. We piled into my brand new Scion—birthday present from the old man—and drove the two blocks to our favorite hangout. With music blaring and wheels spinning, we sped toward the waiting lattes and Frappaccinos.

It was going to be a long night—a little caffeine would do us good. The after party would probably go until early in the morning and we would need every ounce of artificial energy we could get.

You know those after parties. What usually happens after the after party is a hangover. Somebody's always sneaking in a little something to spike up, er, I mean spice up the night.

After all we had earned it. We were all looking to blow off a little steam! We three seniors at Brentwood High School were riding high and just a few months away from ultimate freedom—AKA graduation. Four years at one of the academically toughest high schools in the city and we'd all made it, mostly with flying colors. Maybe this time I could even talk Nick into coming.

Little did I know that the next hour or so at Starbucks would ruin my plans for good.

That night's performance of *Grease* was a big deal to all of us. While none of us were in the musical itself, the missing person in our foursome was. Kailey was playing the lead role of Sandy and we couldn't wait to cheer her on from the front row. The "*Look at me, I'm Sandra D*" jokes had been flowing since she got the part of Sandy after winter break. Kailey took it all with a great big smile. She'd had bit roles in past plays and musicals but this was her shot at glory. She was hoping that this would be her breakout role and that people, outside of us, her little circle of friends, would notice her. Down deep inside she was hoping that this role would lead to a drama scholarship— or something.

Oh yeah, I almost forgot to introduce myself. My name is Jared. Let's see, how would I describe myself? I don't want to brag...okay, I'll brag just a little. I'm a good looking jock, tall and quasi ripped (100 push ups a day will do that!). Let's just say I've never had a problem getting a date.

Track is my sport of choice. I run pretty freakin' fast. As a matter of fact, a few months ago I snagged a scholarship to our state college, full ride! Dad tried to act happy, but I think he was disappointed I didn't get a full ride at USC like Jake (my big brother). Dad didn't say anything, but he wears his disappointment like his cologne...thick.

My dad can crush you with a raised eyebrow. I know from personal experience. His non-verbal smirks have smashed my ego many times.

Never good enough. Never fast enough. Never smart enough.

Even my 3.7 GPA isn't good enough for dad. Jake made the 4.0 'hall of fame' in our house, so by falling short of perfection by .3, I'd failed to measure up. But enough about me. I'm depressing myself.

I want to tell you a little about the friends that were with me in my car that night. (Did I mention my new Scion?)

Jen is one of the school's 'pretty girls'. But unlike most of them she isn't stuck-up. She's down to earth and real. She gives it to you straight and hard when she thinks you're full of it. Her long blond hair and flashing blue eyes can lead you to believe that she's just a pretty face, but there's more to her than meets the eye.

Jen loves to have fun. To be honest, she has a little bit of a bad girl in her. I've noticed recently that she's been looking for love in all the wrong places. She's a hottie who knows all the right people and goes to all the right parties. She's gotten in trouble a few times for some of the things she's inhal...I mean tried. But, for the most part, Jen is working harder than usual, trying to get her act together for graduation.

Jen's family situation is radically different from mine. Her mom is a devout Catholic and her dad is a devoted alcoholic. She has chosen a party 'purgatory' in between. But, in her words, she leans more toward daddy's hell than mom's heaven. Jen told me once that she's just out for all the fun she can get—just like you're supposed to do at this age. But sometimes she just seems really confused about life.

Me? Inwardly, I like Jen's rebellious streak. She is the one who has pulled me into the partying scene, though I am more careful than her, because, well, I'm a jock and don't want to tick off my ultra-conservative track coach. After all, logic and ambition are the twin pillars of how I was taught to live—no religious background at all. Dad is always overbooked on the weekends, so even if we did believe in God we probably would never go to church. Dad is too busy worshipping at the Church of the Almighty Dollar.

I guess if you were to put a religious label on me, it would be 'atheist'. I really don't believe in God. To be honest, I don't know how a God that is good could allow so much suffering in the world.

I was in Mexico last year on a rare family vacation. Somehow we got lost in the barrio and I witnessed poverty like I couldn't believe. Little children covered in grime living in shanties and shacks—everyone drinking from the same dirty stream of garbage-filled water. I guess it shook me up a little bit.

At that moment I decided deep down that if there was a God, he was cruel or, at the very minimum, distant and uncaring. I didn't want to have anything to do with him. The way I saw it, if he wasn't going to be there for me, then why would I want to be there for him.

But that presents a problem. Why? Because my long-time track buddy and best friend on the planet is a blatant Christian. He is the final person in our foursome and the heart and soul of our little quirky clique.

Now 99% of the Christians that I've met over the years at school seemed to fall in one of two categories: they're either whacked-out or hypocrites. The nut jobs are easy to pick out. These are the kids that wear Christ on their sleeves (some literally!). They generally act like they have all the answers and take on the science teachers with talk of Adam, Eve and stories about 'intelligent design' (whatever that is...I wouldn't call whoever 'designed' the duck-billed platypus all that intelligent!). But I digress... Anyway, these Jesus-loving teenagers stand around flagpoles, demand their rights, and walk the halls in their mostly weird, cheesy t-shirts.

I remember one guy in particular who always invited me to go to youth group with him. He was relentless and, to be honest, quite annoying. He would always be telling me that it was bowling night or pizza night or game night. To be honest, it all sounded a little Amish to me.

I know the real reason that he wanted me there was to give me a Jesus sales pitch and convert me from my 'heathen ways'. I remember thinking that he would have more of a chance if he'd just talked about God with me. I never could understand Christians that try to trick you into saying some words and becoming part of 'the fold'. It always felt kind of manipulative.

The other kind of Christian is annoying for a whole different reason. Hypocrites are easy to spot. They claim the label of Jesus, but don't follow a word of what he said. When they're with their little Christian friends, they look and talk and act like Christians. But I've seen many of them at the same parties I go to. They're usually the first to grab a drink and the last to stagger out. Ironically, more wasted than me...

Like I said, 99% of the Christians I've ever met are either whacked-out or hypocrites.

That leaves the 1%.

That leaves Nick.

It's kind of hard to describe Nick. Starting freshman year, we were on the track team together—same relay team—so our friendship was born out of sweat and shared dreams. He's not part of the 'in crowd' of Southern California cool. He's usually in serious need of a haircut, and his build is more lanky than ripped, but there's something genuine about him that I like—no, that I respect.

Maybe it's because when he asks you "how are you doing?" he really means it. He seems to treat everyone like he really cares. Or maybe it's because I've never seen him compromise his values, not once—believe me, I've tried to get him to! Maybe it's because I know that he's really sold out to his beliefs. I don't buy it or really understand it, but I know he does…hook, line and sinker. His sincerity draws me in. He's not fake. This is why I like hanging with Nick.

Now don't get me wrong, he and I have pulled our share of pranks. But I haven't seen him cross the line. Well, he got mad once, really mad at me for something I said. I'll never forget him coming to me the next day and asking my forgiveness. I'd never had anyone genuinely ask me for forgiveness for anything. Even though we go way back, it kinda left me stunned. I wish my dad and I could have just one moment like that. But the pride is so thick in our house that if it were smoke, we'd all suffocate.

I guess it's part of being Christian or something—converting the heathen—because Nick has tried to talk with me about God several times. I know some Bible stories and they just sound like a bunch of fairy tales to me. So I've just shut Nick down every time he's tried to bring it up. I've always just told him no offense, but I'm not into the whole religion thing. He'd always come back with, "But I'm not talking about religion, I'm talking about Jesus!"

My response? None. I'd just clam up until he'd shut up…and he always did.

So here we were, three unlikely friends pushing open the door to our favorite Starbucks, killing some time before the show. The air was electric. Spring was upon us and one of our best friends was starring in *Grease*.

2

The familiar Starbucks smells and sounds greeted us as we queued up—home away from home. We ordered, and friendly banter took over as we waited for the hot female barista to make our even hotter drinks.

"I'm kinda thinkin' I'm becoming a caffeine addict," Nick commented as he grabbed his latte from the counter.

"Yeah, Christian crack!" Jen shot back.

We all laughed. Jen is quick with the zingers and is continually, but good-naturedly, making fun of Nick and his straight-up lifestyle.

After the rest of us retrieved our caffeinated concoctions, we staked our claim on the big comfortable chairs in the corner—the quietest part of this particular Starbucks, where the half wall separated us from the loud WHIRRING sound of the mega espresso machine.

For a few minutes our conversation was focused on Kailey and *Grease*. We all took pride in Kailey's stardom. We had all taken our turn at listening to her vent about all the drama queens she'd put up with in rehearsals these past months. But we'd supported and encouraged her along the way, just like our clique always did for each other. Tonight, she would be representing us all up there.

But a few sips into our conversation the pleasant small talk took an unexpected turn to the risky subject of religion. And much to my surprise, I was at the steering wheel.

It was the headline of the coffee-stained *New York Times* on the little table next to our cushy chairs that caught my attention. I reached over while Jen and Nick were joking around about something and read the six bold words across the top of the newspaper:

Top Evangelical Pastor Caught in Adultery

After skimming the front page article, I couldn't contain my disgust and let loose my own six startling words, "All Christians are just plain hypocrites!"

As I spewed out these words with more venom than I had originally intended, both Jen and Nick looked around at me with a jerk. I flung the paper across the coffee table toward Nick...just to get a rise out of him. Like a Vegas Blackjack dealer's card throw, the paper slid across the table and landed right in front of him.

He picked up the article and started reading it. As he did, he was subconsciously shaking his head. He had a pained look on his face.

"Whoa. Whoa. Whoa, just kidding, Nick," I pleaded, "don't cry or anything, dude. I was just messing with you." But Nick sat there in silence, ignoring my jab.

"What's wrong?" Jen asked.

"This makes me sick!" Nick exploded. "This guy is supposed to be a pastor, and he's out doing stuff like this. What was he thinking? How stupid is he?"

"Calm down, man," I ventured.

"You don't get it, Jared." Nick was seething. "I know what it's like to have your parents screw up and totally mess your life up right along with their own. Look at this picture of him with his wife and kids with the media swarming. Think of this guy's kids. They look totally shell-shocked."

Nick barely came up for a breath before he continued on. "Remember, my mom's been through three husbands and counting—this is personal. Every time my mom heads into one of her 'romantic relationships', I cringe and brace myself for what I know is coming in the end—disaster. It's gotta be ten times worse to go through it all in full view of the media and the whole world, for that matter."

It was the weirdest thing. All of a sudden the anger seemed to just drain out of him and his voice softened. "Didn't he think about how much cheating on his wife would hurt his family, his church, the reputation of God himself...

"Wait a minute," Nick continued quietly. "What am I doing here, who am I to pass judgment on him...that's God's job, not mine. After all, I'm a hypocrite too, just like him," he said with absolute seriousness.

Friends for such a long time and I still get surprised by Nick. Of all the words I expected out of his mouth, I didn't think he'd be lumping himself in with this preacher. To be honest, I really just wanted to diffuse this religion talk and move on. The last thing I wanted was to leave the door open for a long-winded response. We'd been having a great time. Before I could say anything, Jen beat me to the punch.

"You're not a hypocrite, Nick. Come on, dude, if every Christian were like you then maybe I'd become one too."

"I am a hypocrite, Jen. I haven't gone out and committed adultery like this guy or anything, but I know that I consistently screw up what God wants for my life. Look at me just now… it's obvious I'm not a very forgiving person. You can tell I still get angry at my mom and the mess she's made of her life. And that's just the beginning. I can't possibly live up to the message of Jesus consistently. I've lied. I've lusted. I'm obviously still bitter. I fall short everyday."

Trying to break the silence and move the conversation on I joked, "You've lusted? Have you ever lusted after Jen? Or is it me that you want?"

Have you ever told a joke that fell like a steaming turd on the sidewalk? Well, that was what happened. Jen and Nick continued talking like the turd never fell.

And then it just got quiet, painfully quiet.

The awkward silence was palpable as we all just sat there, no one talking, everyone sipping. Nick continued reading the newspaper article. Jen, who doesn't like conflict, was kind of staring off in space. Afraid of saying something stupid again, I just chose to keep my mouth shut.

Nick finally broke the quiet, "For me, Christianity is not a club or a philosophy or a religious ideal that I must live up to, it's a relationship with Jesus that is continually changing me from the inside out. It's a growing process. But the process is never finally complete and because of that, in some ways, Christians always fall short of what Jesus intended. It's in that sense that every Christian, including me, is a hypocrite."

My brain was racing in a bunch of directions and all at the same time. Here was one of the most considerate guys on the planet, in my experience, telling me he was a hypocrite. Sometimes Christians just didn't make sense.

16

First, they try to live up to a standard that they agree no one can keep. They all talk about 'believing in Jesus', but in the next breath say you have to have some kind of 'relationship' with a guy who's been dead for a couple of thousand years. I couldn't remember anyone, anywhere saying that being a hypocrite was OK with God...if you believe in God.

Jen's reply pulled me out of my head and back into the conversation. "I think you're being way too tough on yourself, Nick. Sometimes people do things that are unforgivable. When my dad's on one of his binges, he says stuff that's burned into my memory forever. Things I can't forgive or forget. If you ask me, none of us needs to forgive our parents for the hell they've put us through. They don't deserve it."

"You don't understand, Jen," Nick countered. "Forgiveness is at the center of Jesus' teachings and what he came to earth to do. Sometimes I'm still not very good at forgiveness. But like I said, it's a process, it takes time..."

"That kind of makes sense," Jen said. "If Jesus 'saves' you or whatever from your sins I guess it takes a little time...but when the pain is really screaming, I just can't forgive and make it all go away." After a brief pause she added, "Sounds kind of hopeless to me."

Nick came back strong with, "It's not hopeless at all because—"

I cut him off. I knew he was about to launch into his whole religion verses relationship talk, so I decided to throw him a curve ball. "Okay, since we're being honest here, let me ask you an honest question, Nick."

"Go ahead," he replied.

Scooting forward on my chair, I looked straight in his eyes and asked, "If Christianity is for hypocrites, why did you get so shook up when you looked at that newspaper article? I mean, it shouldn't have surprised you, right?" Expecting that I'd landed a direct hit, I sat back and waited for his response.

3

"Because I get sick of it," was Nick's blunt, honest answer.

"Sick of what?" Jen asked with a confused look on her face.

"Sick of the message Christians are sending to the world! Yes, we all fall short of what Jesus intended, but guys like this don't even seem to be trying to serve Jesus, and it makes me mad!

"This preacher was known in the media for railing against homosexual sin," Nick went on. "He organized petitions to get civil unions among homosexuals outlawed and all that jazz. The article says that he was the largest single voice in getting gay marriage banned in several states all across America. Meanwhile, he's been cheating on his wife. Too many times we're sending the message that Christianity is a list of rules and regulations that must be kept by everyone else. Meanwhile, we're breaking the rules ourselves."

"Wait a minute," Jen interrupted, "isn't the Christian religion all about 'the rules'? I mean isn't that what all religions are? My mom is a full on Catholic. I don't know all that much about what she believes, 'cause it's kinda a forbidden topic around our house. When I was really little, I raised a fuss once about having to go to church with her, and my dad told me I didn't need to go, and I haven't gone back since I was like six years old.

"Lots of fights about that between my parents," Jen continued, rolling her eyes. "But the way I understand it, my mom *has* to go to confession, to Mass, pray to Mary, say the Rosary, and who knows what else. She's got all sorts of rules and regulations that she thinks she has to keep in order to pass the big test and make it to heaven someday."

Nick countered, "Jen, God doesn't care if you're Catholic or Baptist or whatever. It doesn't matter which church you go to. God doesn't look at the team we're on. But everyone trusts something in their life. He judges us based on what we're trusting our lives to, whether it's ourselves, the rules we put our faith in, something else, or him. It's what a person does with Jesus that matters."

I knew it was coming. The relationship speech Nick had been trying to give me for years was on. Jen seemed more interested in this stuff than I thought she'd be, so this time it looked like there was nothing I could do about it.

What I did know about religion and rules didn't seem to fit with where Nick was heading, though. I knew enough to realize that rules don't go very far in making for a good relationship. If my latest girlfriend made a rule that I had to love her, how lame would that be? A one-sided, cold relationship. I'd be like a robot.

Jen interrupted my thoughts by asking, "What do you mean by 'does with Jesus'? And what could Jesus possibly have to do with the decisions I make in my life?"

Nick thought for awhile and began, "Well, there are two types of people who call themselves 'Christians' out there. One is the 'rules Christian' who sees Jesus as a good example that they must live up to, and then maybe, just maybe, meet someday in heaven... if they're good enough that is."

"And the other type?" I asked.

"The other type is the type that knows that there is no possible way we could ever live up to the example of Jesus, so we give up trying—"

"Whoa! Wait a minute!" I interrupted, "I'm an atheist and even I don't think a person should give up trying to be like Jesus. Besides, isn't this a part of being in the 'Christian club'?"

"Let me explain, Jared. I wasn't finished. The other type of Christian, the true Christian, is the one who knows following all the rules is impossible. Instead, they give up trying to be like Jesus and start trusting him with their life."

"I don't understand," exclaimed Jen.

"*We* don't understand," I emphasized.

"Okay, let me back up a little bit so we can get the big picture, okay?" Nick offered.

"Sure, you've been wanting to tell me the 'gospel story' or whatever for awhile anyway, haven't you?" I said with a smile on my face.

"Yeah, but every time I try, you shut me down, bro!"

"You're on stage now, better go for it," I said while glancing over at Jen's nodding head and riveted eyes. "As a matter of fact, I'll probably have a few questions along the way that I may drill you with, if that's okay."

"Sure!" Nick said. "Bring it, Atheist!"

We all laughed together, but the look of intensity in Nick's eyes made me a little uncomfortable. I knew I didn't have all the answers. But I was confident that I was not going to let him push me into some twisted logic corner and convert me. It was best to let him know that up front.

"Just don't get your feelings hurt when I grill you," I warned.

"Jared!" Jen scolded, throwing a stir stick at me.

"I'm kidding! I'm kidding!" I blurted, while ducking the tiny projectile. But I really wasn't.

"Before I share this story with you, I want to make one thing perfectly clear," Nick announced with uncharacteristic assertiveness.

"What's that?" asked Jen.

"I'm not going to try to force either of you to buy into Christianity, real Christianity, that is. I'm just going to paint a picture that you can choose to either accept or reject."

I responded right away. "Fair enough, and I won't try to convert you to atheism, I'll just paint a picture of atheism for you that you can choose to accept or reject."

"Agreed." Jen and Nick said almost simultaneously.

"Well, the story starts in a garden," Nick began.

"Wait! No 'once upon a time' or anything?" Jen giggled.

"No. Because it's not a fairy tale, Jen," Nick responded with a slight smile.

"Let me guess, the Garden of Eden, right?" I said, trying to get the conversation back on track, figuring the quicker we got through this the better.

"Right!" Nick answered.

"So you're one of those 'creationism freaks' are you, Nick? Come on, bro, I thought you were brighter than that!" I could tell my words stung a bit, but I had my limits.

Before Nick could respond, Jen interrupted, "Wait a minute, what exactly do you mean by 'creationism'?"

I think I surprised Nick when I jumped in. "Creationism is the belief that God created everything in the universe in six days. Christians believe that there were no cavemen or stuff like that. But they think that God made all the animals and created the first man and woman, Adam and Eve, on the sixth day. He put them in a beautiful place called the Garden of Eden where they lived in peace and harmony, walking around naked eating apples."

Proud of myself, I asked, "Isn't that right, Nick?"

I could tell Nick was surprised I knew this much. Finally he asked me, "Where did you learn all that? Did you go to Sunday school when you were little?"

"Nah!" I answered. "The only time I've ever been on the inside of a church was for my cousin's wedding. I learned it from the Christian nerds in my science classes the last three years at Brentwood! I've heard all their little arguments. They're idiots!"

Nick responded calmly, but his words stung a bit, "I'm one of those idiots, Jared."

Jen's eyes turned toward me and I knew I was in a good spot, so I started to defend my position by attacking his. "Come on, Nick. You don't really buy into all that stuff about Adam and Eve in an environmentally friendly garden of bliss, do you? There is so much evidence for evolution, denying it is stupid."

Nick was quiet for a moment and then out of nowhere he said, "I've got to use the bathroom." With that he quickly grabbed his backpack and walked off.

4

Jen and I just kind of sat there, surprised at how abruptly Nick had left.

"That was weird," Jen whispered.

"Well, when you got to pee, you got to pee," I whispered back.

Reaching over I found his Venti empty. "The boy's got a Grande bladder, but is living in a Venti world," I cracked.

Jen laughed so hard she snorted. The guys who had been checking her out earlier were checking her out again, but this time for a different reason.

While she was pulling herself together, I started thinking again about Nick. Nick—a creationist nerd?! This was embarrassing. Believing in God was one thing, but not seeing the obvious, was another. What was he thinking? Anyway, Jen would back me up. Besides, first question and he was already running scared.

After a few minutes Nick came back and asked if we could all move to the table. We agreed. As we grabbed our drinks, I started giving Nick a hard time for bringing his backpack into the bathroom with him. "Don't you trust us, dude? Think I'm going to steal your Bible or something?"

He just laughed. It was kind of weird when Nick just stood there and waited for us to be seated first at one of the bigger round tables. He then took the seat directly across from Jen and me. But before I could say anything, Nick jumped back in.

"Okay, first off, there are lots of beliefs within Christianity. I know it may seem to you like Christianity is just one set of beliefs, but Christians write lots of books about Creationism and Intelligent Design and a bunch of other theories about how everything in the universe began.

"As I said before," Nick continued, "Christianity is a relationship. But every relationship has to start somewhere in history. Christians believe that a long time ago God created the first people and gave them a choice to trust him or not, just like we have the same kind of choice today. So, some Christians believe God used evolution to create these very first people and everything on the earth. And some Christians think that God created the entire universe out of nothing by literally speaking it into existence."

"What do you believe?" I asked.

"I believe that God created everything out of nothing in six days, like those idiots in your biology class," Nick replied. "You know me, I'm not easily convinced about anything and we can talk more about how I came to my conclusions another time. But the most important part to remember is that all Christians believe that the earth and all the life on it didn't just happen randomly, it was part of God's plan. And people and their choices are part of God's plan too."

I just sat there shaking my head in disbelief. I couldn't get past the thought that Nick was one of those creation nerds. "So all of our science teachers are caught up in some kind of worldwide conspiracy?" I challenged.

"No. Well, yes," Nick came back. "I think that some theories have the effect of pointing people away from the reality of a Creator."

"I don't know, Nick. Sounds pretty far out to me. I was always told that the earth is billions of years old because it would take billions of years for all of this stuff to evolve. But you're saying that God created everything in like six days," Jen replied.

"I just have to interrupt, Nick," I jumped back in headfirst, ready for a fight. "Evolutionists *know* from fossil studies that dinosaurs lived millions of years ago."

"And they know that because...?" Nick patiently asked.

"Because they've dated them back that far," I replied.

"And how do they do that?" Nick asked.

"Carbon dating and that stuff we learned about in bio class," I shrugged.

Suddenly Nick's head went down. His hands were under the table and he just stared downward like he was deep in thought. Jen and I just looked at each other. There must have been like sixty seconds of very awkward silence at the table. But by now we had both gotten used to these awkward moments in our brief time at Starbucks. I thought that maybe it was a 'Christian' thing or something. I didn't want to be disrespectful. Maybe he was praying.

"Scientists like to think they know what they know," Nick said as his head came back up. "But think back to a couple hundred years ago, when scientists didn't even know about sub-atomic particles. I have no doubt that there's a lot science doesn't even know it doesn't know. And a way for figuring out the age of the earth could be one of those things scientists haven't quite nailed down yet."

"But all that stuff we learned in bio class and took tests over...there's plenty of other proof that evolution is true," I challenged.

"No, there's not," was Nick's uncharacter-istically blunt response.

Girding myself for another showdown I asked, "What do you mean there's no proof?"

"There's no real proof of evolution or creation," Nick stated. "There's evidence on both sides, some that you can point to, and some that I can point to. But the bottom line is that neither you nor I can recreate macroevolution or creationism in the science lab."

Jen tried to break the tension we were all feeling. "Macroevolution? Is that short for macaroni? Because I can tell you right now that my macaroni underwent evolution when I added cheese to it and left it in the microwave too long."

Our collective laughter broke the tension once more. I noticed that Nick's head dropped again. It seemed like it was becoming routine. Maybe it was the way Nick centered himself or something, kind of like the lotus meditation position for Christians.

"Let me put it this way, Jared," Nick said, jerking the conversation back toward the serious, "I believe that God created everything in six days, right?"

"If you say so," I agreed.

"And you believe that macroevolution is true," Nick continued, "the kind that turned an amoeba into a tadpole into a frog into a reptile into a monkey into a man over the course of millions of years. Right?"

"Yes," I flatly stated.

"But neither of us can reproduce this in the lab. So, both you and I are exercising faith in believing what we believe."

"That's where you're wrong, Nick!" I knew that I had him now. "It has been scientifically proven that all sorts of creatures evolve. Moths evolve and change. Different kinds of tigers look differently in different regions. The same is true with bears. Look at the polar bear versus the grizzly bear. I could go on and on about how animals adapt and change, Nick. Even people evolve! Look at the physical differences between Eskimos and Pigmies."

Head down. Jesus-loving lotus position again, this time for thirty seconds and then bam, he was back in.

"Yes. You're right." Nick stated. "I guess I do believe in evolution—microevolution, some call it 'adaptation', the changing characteristics of an animal or an insect or a reptile or a bird within a species. I have no problem with adaptation. It's macroevolution that I have a problem with, changing from one species to another. Charles Darwin himself boldly stated that if evolution was true, then scientists would discover millions of transitional species in excavations around the globe. And, like I said before, they've found zero, nada, zilch."

When I looked at Jen I could tell she was puzzled before she asked her question. "But not all Christians believe God created the earth in six days?"

"No," Nick responded. "Many believe that God oversaw the process of evolution to create everything on the earth. But I figure that if the Bible says that God created the world in six days, then it was six days."

"Blind faith?" I asked with just a hint of sarcasm.

"Not blind faith," Nick answered. "I think God provides enough evidence so that I'm not taking a blind leap of faith. As a matter of fact, I think it's a leap into the light and not the darkness."

It was quiet for a few seconds and then Nick said something that caught me off guard. "I'm sorry, guys."

"Why?" Jen asked. "I don't know why, but we don't talk about important things like this very often."

Nick began again, "Well, we kinda got off the subject. My intention was not to get into a debate about evolution versus creation. Being Christian means trusting Jesus, and not a bunch of scientists."

I interrupted with my best Godfatheresque voice, "Fah-get-a-bout-it. After all we're the ones who were asking the questions about creationism. But if you aren't trying to prove creationism to us, then what are you trying to prove?"

"That both you and I have faith in something. You trust that blind fate over billions of years made our universe, every animal, bug and human through evolution. I trust that the Bible is true and that God created everything in this universe. All of us have to have some level of faith to believe what we believe. Right?"

"Yeah, I guess so," I responded. "I've never seen myself as a person of faith. But in that sense, I guess I kind of am."

Nick pulled his chair closer to the table and continued, "So if each of us exercises faith, my question to you is, which takes more faith to believe, that an infinite God created everything that exists, or that the incredible complexities of the universe and our bodies happened by mere chance?

Neither Jen nor I had a quick answer, so Nick continued, "Let me explain it a different way. Let's say I took your watch apart and separated it all out into a hundred pieces. Let's say I took all those pieces and put them in a paper sack. I shake the bag up, dig a hole and bury it. Let's say I come back in fifty years and dig that bag up. What are the chances of that watch being put back together all by itself."

"Zero to none," was Jen's reply.

"Jared?" asked Nick.

"I'll tell you something right now," I joked, "if you took my watch apart and put it in a bag and buried it, then I'd take you apart and bury you, dude. I got that thing at Nordstrom's. That watch is worth more than my life!"

"Oh, you must have gotten it on sale!" Jen cracked.

We all started laughing once again. For as intense as this conversation was, we'd had several laugh breaks.

"Okay, okay, Nick, what's your point about my watch in pieces in the paper sack?" I asked.

Nick replied, "All I'm saying is this, Jared. The universe is much more complicated than your watch. DNA, physics, chemistry, planetary orbits, how a body works and a whole bunch of other things are all way more complicated than the theory of evolution can explain. So I believe that God had to be right smack in the middle of the creative process. And I'm not the only one. More and more scientists think that Creationism is a reasonable theory. And even if you believe in evolution, something had to have created the very first stuff that all of life came from—there had to be some sort of first cause that caused the rest."

"Good points. I've got to go pee," was my response. I got up, and urgently headed off, looking for relief.

5

I wasn't sure what to think about this conversation, but it was making me a little uncomfortable. Billions of years, probability and God are all impossible to get your mind around. I agree that no one can know for sure how everything got started. So Nick was right about that, everyone has faith in something.

Maybe there really was some supernatural force that had a hand in creating life. Could there actually be a God? And a bunch of rules we were supposed to follow so God would like us? What if there really was some great judge in the sky that was the extreme version of my dad—always watching me, always judging me, distant and disappointed? The thought was both intriguing and depressing at the same time in an odd sort of way.

When I returned I found Nick and Jen deep in conversation. I just sat down and listened in for a few minutes.

Jen was asking Nick, "I guess I don't understand why all this talk of how everything began matters so much. I thought you were going to tell us the story of Christianity. What does it matter whether we were created or evolved?"

"The first four words in the Bible are 'In the beginning God'," Nick offered. "The rest of the whole Bible and Jesus' part of the story won't make any sense unless you start with those four words. It matters too, because it determines how you view yourself. If you evolved through natural selection then, in one way, you are the result of a pretty cold process. You are who you are. You were born. You live. You're going to die. And then that's it. You're worm food after that. And while you live, it doesn't really matter what you do with your life. After all it's 'survival of the fittest', right?"

"Yeah, I guess," Jen conceded.

"But believing in God makes it a whole different story," Nick went on. "If God made you in his image and for his glory, then you have purpose in your life. You were created by him to be in relationship with him to bring him glory."

Jen interrupted, "What do you mean by that word 'glory'?"

"Sorry, Jen, sometimes Christian words make things impossible to understand. In other words, if God created you, then you have a higher purpose than just living out your eighty-some years and dying, and that is to acknowledge him, serve him and worship him. You have a bigger purpose and deeper meaning for your life, that's the relationship part. In this life we relate to him, and when we die we can spend forever with him in heaven."

When I sensed a pause in the conversation I interrupted, "Hey guys, while I was sitting on the can I thought of another question."

"Ewww. Thanks for the mental picture, Jared!" Jen yelled, hitting me in the arm hard.

"Shoot," said Nick.

"The whole Adam, Eve, apple thing about breaking God's rules—do you really believe all that?" I asked.

"Okay, okay, sorry, I'm having to play Bible catch up again here guys," Jen interrupted, "Will someone please tell me where an apple ties into the story of Christianity?"

I looked over at Nick and asked, "May I?"

"Sure," he said, nodding. "You've been trained by the Bible nerd squad in biology class, right? Go for it."

I began to explain to Jen, "Okay, so God creates Adam and Eve and they're living together in the garden in perfect harmony. Did I mention that they were naked?"

"Yes," answered Jen, "twice now. Why are you so fixated on the word 'naked'?"

I informed her that all guys liked to walk around the house naked and they loved to see naked girls. "God made us guys that way. Right, Nick?"

"I guess so...but I didn't know about the naked house walking stuff," Nick responded. "Maybe that's just an atheist thing, Jared."

I continued, unhindered by the friendly shot, "Anyway, the story goes that Adam and Eve are hanging out in the Garden of Eden and God gave them only one rule to keep. God told them not to eat fruit from the tree of evil—"

"Actually, it was called 'the tree of the knowledge of good and evil', but close enough," interrupted Nick.

"Thanks. So a snake that is possessed by Satan or something, talks Eve into eating the fruit from the tree, and she talks Adam into it and they both realize they're naked," I smiled again at the word, "and they try to hide from God. Is that close enough to the real story, Nick?"

"That's pretty good, Jared! You should teach a Bible study!"

"Don't push it!" I said, attempting to joke.

"But seriously," Nick continued, "that's the story of the first three chapters of the Bible. And here's what the story means. God created people because he wanted to relate to them. But a loving relationship can only exist if it includes the choice not to love. So God gave them a choice, and they chose to go against God. They turned their back on him and ruined the relationship they had with him. Adam and Eve's decision is the same decision to sin that each of us makes all the time."

"Wait. I want to make sure our terms are clear, just exactly what do you mean by that word 'sin'?" Jen asked.

Nick replied, "It means 'to miss the mark' or 'fall short of God's perfect standard.'

It's anything that we do that misses the mark of God's perfection."

"So what happened to Adam and Eve when they chose to sin?" asked Jen.

I'll never forget Nick's blunt reply, because it fed into all my worst fears about a cruel and judgmental God.

"They fell out of relationship with God and were condemned to die. You see, God made Adam and Eve to live forever, but they chose to go their own way and that's how death entered the world. They didn't die right away physically, but they chose to end their relationship with God and died spiritually. In other words they became spiritually corrupted and self-centered. The rest of history shows the consequences of their choice to go their own way—sin all around us: wars, famines, AIDs, broken families, crime."

"So you mean to tell me," I interrupted, "that all the crap in the world is a result of sin?"

"Yes."

"Okay, that's where I got you nailed, Nick!" I exclaimed, pounding the table.

"Hey, calm down man. Remember, we're not debating, we're just having a friendly conversation about God, right?"

But I didn't miss a beat and plowed on, "Okay, a lot of wars throughout history were launched by Christians. Think of the Crusades in Medieval times! Christians have been at the center of a lot of the wars in human history!"

Nick looked down and paused again, not saying anything for a full minute.

"Cricket, cricket," Jen said, trying to break the silence with a little humor.

Finally looking up, Nick asked me, "So what you're saying is that if wars are the result of sin in the world and if Christians were responsible for some of these wars, then Christians are hypocrites?"

"Yes!" I knew that I had him with this one—that high IQ of mine was finally useful.

6

"I agree, Jared. Remember how this whole conversation got started—the newspaper story." Nick glanced over at the newspaper. "I was telling you guys about how far I fall short, too. I'm a Christian and I struggle with sin like everyone else, including you. Since the beginning of time we've all fallen short of what God's wanted us to be. I know that I fall way short. When a Christian sins, and all of us do, it doesn't negate the reality of God, it only shows how much we all need him in our lives."

I glanced at Jen and was surprised to see that she didn't look as skeptical as I was expecting her to.

"All I'm saying is this," Nick continued, "that as a Christian, I have an explanation for the problem of evil. The problem of evil is not God. It's us and our choices. He gave Adam and Eve a free will in the Garden of Eden and they chose to disobey God. We've been choosing to disobey ever since. It's as simple as that."

"But wait a minute, Nick," Jen said. "Just what exactly is the problem of evil? I must have missed that one on the math test."

Nick responded with a series of questions. "Have you ever wondered where evil came from? How did it get into the world and into the human heart? Have you ever wanted to cheat on a test? Have you ever wondered why bad things happen to good people? Why there was something so horribly evil as the Holocaust and stuff like that?"

"Sure, we've all wondered that," was Jen's reply, looking at me to see if I agreed.

Nick continued, "The Bible's answer is that there are no good people." Reaching down to his backpack he began to rummage through his stuff. Finally he pulled out his Bible, opened it up, and said, "What we've been talking about is in the Bible. It says right here in Romans 3:23,

'For all have sinned and fall short of the glory of God.' We have all lost that relationship with God that deep down we want and were created to have."

"Wait a minute, Nick." I interrupted, now getting a little angry. "I know some really bad people, but I also know some good people. My Aunt Sarah is the kindest person I've ever met. She gives money to the poor and volunteers at the Rescue Mission. You mean to tell me she's not a good person?"

Lotus position for Nick again…wait…wait… and then we were back again.

"Good compared to what?" Nick asked.

"What do you mean?" I asked back.

"I mean, I'm sure your Aunt Sarah does all those good things you say and is a good person when you compare her to other people you know. But that's not the kind of good that God talks about. It's when any of us compare ourselves with God that we realize that nobody is truly good."

"Your Aunt Sarah may be good when compared to everyone else you know, but compared to God, we all fall short," Nick continued. "We all miss the mark by a mile. Me, you, Jen and, yes, even your dear Aunt Sarah.

"God judges us, not just on the good deeds we do on the outside, but also on the reason we're doing those deeds. God sees right through our actions into our motives. What he sees is the selfishness that plagues us all—me included. We would all be screwed if we relied on good works to get us to heaven because, at our core, we're all selfish. We're more concerned with ourselves than others."

"Well, I think I'm a good person," I boldly proclaimed. "And I think Jen is too."

"Alright, you're kind of forcing me into this, so I'm going to have to get down and dirty with you. Are you ready?" Nick asked.

"I thought getting down and dirty was against your religion," Jen teased.

"You've heard of the Ten Commandments, right?" Nick inquired.

Both Jen and I responded, "Duhhhhh!"

"Well, these commandments represent what God means when he talks about goodness and what he demands of us all the time, without exception, for all of our lives. Things like, don't put anyone or anything above God in importance in your life. I'm self-centered every day of my life, so check that one off. Or don't steal. And it's not just talking about breaking and entering; it includes things like stealing time from your boss at work by calling your friends while you're on the clock, or stealing answers by cheating on homework or tests. And what about lying?"

Jen and I were quiet as Nick looked up and asked, "So how do you guys do when it comes to keeping the Ten Commandments?"

"Well, I've never murdered or anything like that," I said, trying to justify myself.

"Are you sure about that?" Nick was really pushing now. "Jesus said in Matthew 5 that if you hate your brother, you've murdered him in your heart. All of us have pictured ourselves strangling someone we're angry with. I know there have been a few times I've mentally strangled you, Jared."

We all laughed, but this was uncomfortable ground for me. My dad had been sending me the message for years that I didn't measure up, and now my best friend was telling me the same thing…I was not good enough.

Nick continued, "Jesus also said in Matthew 5 that if you've lusted after a girl in your heart then, it's like you've had virtual sex with her and broken the spirit of these commandments. These are just a few of the Ten Commandments, and all of us have already blown it. No offense, but God's standard of pure goodness is something no one can live up to. It's why we need him in our lives."

No laughter this time.

"I'll tell you how I do," Nick went on. "I miss the mark continuously. I fell short of meeting God's perfect standard several times today."

"Murder someone have you?" I asked with a slight smile.

"No, but the night is young," Nick zinged back. "And since we got here, I've been jealous of your new Scion, I've been eyeing the hot barista way too many times, I flipped out about the preacher and ranted through all my old baggage about my mom…need I go on?"

"She is hot, isn't she?" I said, looking over at the barista. I was totally with him on that point.

"So let me get this straight," Jen quickly pushed on. She obviously wasn't interested in our hot barista banter. "You're saying because Adam and Eve screwed up in the garden that all of us are, well, screwed?"

"I might have put it differently, but yes," Nick agreed. "When Adam and Eve sinned, they immediately covered themselves in fig leaves and hid themselves from God in the Garden of Eden."

"Why?" Jen asked.

Nick responded, "Because they knew they had broken the commandment of God not to eat of the tree of the knowledge of good and evil. And for the first time they felt guilty and ashamed—that's why they hid themselves from God.

"And humanity has been playing hide and seek from God ever since. It's like we want to go our own way and do our thing, separate from God, but there's still something deep inside us that feels incomplete apart from him. Like I get this empty feeling whenever I think about my father. I've told you before how I never knew my real dad. He and my mom were never married. Mom was kind of a partier and I was, well, one of the results of her lifestyle.

"So I have this empty spot inside of me, maybe because we're supposed to have a dad in our lives who cares about us," Nick continued. I glanced at Jen, a little concerned about how she was reacting to all this dad talk, since it was always a touchy subject with her. "Well, same thing with God. We're designed to have a relationship with God and when Adam and Eve messed up way back, they messed that up for all of us."

"I sorta know how you feel about the whole having a Dad that's checked out routine," Jen said. "But I still don't get how what Adam and Eve did affects me."

"Well, the way my youth leader explained it was with a bottle of water and a drop of arsenic," Nick offered. "If you let that water bottle represent all of humanity and the poisonous arsenic represent the sin Adam and Eve introduced into the world, it's like they put a drop of arsenic in the water bottle. Would you

take a drink of water that had only one drop of
arsenic in it?"

"No," Jen responded.

"Why?" Nick asked.

"Because it would kill you," she answered.

"And that's exactly what Adam and Eve's
one sin did to the rest of humanity—it poisoned
them spiritually. We were poisoned by sin from
the time we were conceived. Think about it. You
don't have to teach little kids how to be bad—
that comes naturally! You have to teach them
how to play nice—that doesn't come naturally!
Make sense?"

Jen answered, "I guess so. But to say that we
all fall short of God's perfect standard seems
pretty harsh."

"Too harsh," I interjected. "I thought
Christians believe that God is loving and
forgiving. I'm not seein' the love here."

"He is," Nick said with a hint of frustration.
"God is not like us, he is totally love but he is
also totally justice at the same time. He is so
pure that he can't be around sin."

"Kind of like Superman and Kryptonite?" I inserted, half joking.

"Yeah, I guess so. Except God is not weakened by sin, he's just ticked off and hurt by it," Nick replied.

Jen continued, "And you're saying that no matter how many good things we do, we can never offset the bad ones we've already done?"

Nick took a huge swig of his bottled water before he answered simply, "Yes."

"So, I give up," I pushed back, "I mean the picture you're painting for us to accept or reject is pretty depressing. God made us. We screwed up. We're going to die, stand before some kind of divine judgment which, of course, we will fail, and probably end up going to hell and there's nothing we can do to change the situation. I mean, it all sounds kind of empty and hopeless."

"And that's the difference between religion and the good news that Jesus talked about," Nick stated with what I think was a sense of relief that I'd gotten to this conclusion on my own.

At this point I wasn't feeling very good, and it wasn't the Frap. I agreed that I'm not perfect, no one is. But it kinda seemed like God had set us up to fail.

"Okay, now I'm the confused one," Jen interrupted, "what do you mean?"

Nick explained, "Religion conveniently says that you can be good enough, that you can earn your way to heaven, that you can make it on your own. But the Bible says you can't make it, that you are not good enough, that you are hopeless."

"I'm failing to get the 'good news' here," I mumbled. This was not making sense.

"Before you can fully appreciate the good news you have to fully embrace the bad news. The antidote to the arsenic is only good news to those who know they've been poisoned. The cure to cancer is only good news to you if you realize that you have cancer. This is where Jesus comes into the story. And Jesus is only good news to those who recognize that they have the incurable cancer of sin in their souls and are looking for the cure. Does that make sense?" asked Nick.

"Not really. Not yet. Keep going and I'll tell you when I get it," Jen admitted.

Nick continued, "Of all we've talked about up to now, the most important part is that the message of Christianity is the message of what Jesus said and did. And the message of Jesus was that you and I miss the mark, that we can never earn our way to heaven or into God's favor on our own. We miss the mark and are condemned, like Adam and Eve, to die. But God's remedy is that he loved us so much that he sent his only Son, Jesus Christ, into the world to die in our place for our sin."

I interrupted, "Yeah, yeah, yeah...we all know the story. Jesus suffered, died and rose from the dead three days later. It all just seems morbid to me."

"It's more morbid than you think," Nick agreed. "Jesus was beaten with a whip again and again and again—a whip that had pieces of nails and broken pottery tied into it. Soldiers beat him until he was ripped and bloody. After all this, they nailed him to a cross where he hung for six hours naked, bleeding and dying. It's much more morbid than most people imagine. You see those nice little crosses with an image of Jesus hanging gently on the cross and an expression of peace on his face. It was nothing like that. Jesus was assaulted over and over and over again. His death was incredibly brutal. But he did it willingly."

"Okay, so I have a question for you. Why did God have to pick that way to forgive the sins of humanity? Why couldn't he have snapped his fingers and wiped out all the sins of everyone instead of crucifying his own Son? After all, he is God?" After I asked this question, I could tell by Nick's stunned expression that he was thrown for a loop.

"Time for another bathroom break!" Nick almost shouted, leaving his empty water bottle but grabbing his backpack and almost running off toward the bathroom.

"Something's going on with Nick," Jen said.

"Yeah, what's the deal? I wonder what's in that backpack." I asked. "And what do you think is up with all the meditative lotus position poses he's been pulling?"

"Why don't we try to find out?" Jen suggested with a conspiratorial smile.

I agreed. Anyway, the conversation had been getting so serious we needed something to lighten up the tone. He had been putting his pack on the floor right next to where he'd been sitting. Our plan was to use our feet under the table to slide the pack slowly toward one of us, whoever it was closer to, next time he was in one of his meditative poses.

We were determined to get to the bottom of Nick's weirdness about his backpack.

7

"Alright, where were we?" Nick asked, throwing his backpack down on the chair next to him and unknowingly thwarting our plans.

Temporarily thrown off by the location of his backpack, I kind of stumbled, "Uhh, uhh... we were talking about—"

Jen came to my rescue. "We were talking about why Jesus had to die such a horrible death on the cross to pay for the sins of humanity and why God couldn't have just snapped his fingers and forgiven everyone."

Nick looked at Jen and asked, "The way Jesus died really bothers you doesn't it, Jen?"

Jen shot back without hesitation, "Yeah, it does."

"Why?" Nick asked.

"Well, I hate violence and it's hard for me to imagine a God who would allow this level of violence on his own Son because everyone else screwed up," Jen admitted.

"Me too, Jen. It's hard for me to imagine that. But let me tell you about the very first verse in the Bible that I ever heard. It's John 3:16, and it goes like this: 'For God so loved the world that he gave his one and only Son, that whoever believes in him shall not perish but have eternal life.' God gave up Jesus to this violent, painful death because he loves us and wants to reestablish the relationship with us that was lost when Adam and Eve sinned. In that relationship we can trust him, glorify him, have a purpose in life and live forever with him in heaven."

I could tell that Nick's words touched Jen deeply. And, to be honest, they kind of moved me too. For the first time, I thought to myself that if Christianity were really true it would be the greatest love story ever, a God who would allow his Son to be slaughtered so he could repair the relationship and be reunited with humanity.

But I wasn't ready to buy what my friend was trying to sell.

"You never answered the question, Nick," I reminded him, breaking up the semi-solemn moment.

"What question?" Nick asked.

"Why did Jesus have to die? Why couldn't God just snap his fingers and forgive everyone?" I reminded him.

"Oh yeah," he said. "I did forget. The reason that Jesus had to die was because God is a God of justice. He set the world up so that there is cause and effect, and that means there are consequences for our bad choices and behaviors. In other words, he had to make things right. Since it is impossible for humans to make things right on their own, he had to make it right for them by sacrificing his own Son in their place. Think of it in a courtroom setting. Jared, let's say you get a speeding ticket—"

Jen interrupted, "That's not hard to imagine. You think you're Dale Earnhardt, Jr. in your new Scion!"

"No, I'm Ricky Bobby, driving with a bobcat!" I shot back.

Nick continued, "Better listen up, Jared, or I'll come at you like a spider monkey!"

Jen got us back on track as we were about to go on a wild Will Ferrell tangent by saying, "Okay, okay, sorry I got us sidetracked, so Jared gets a speeding ticket."

Still laughing a little, Nick continued, "Yeah, Jared gets a ticket but can't afford to pay the fine. He is about to get sentenced to jail for his unpaid ticket but you, being the great girl that you are, pay his fine for him. He goes free because you paid his fine. That's what Jesus did. He paid our outstanding fine for us and we go free if we put our faith and trust in him."

Jen added, "Except our 'ticket' is not for speeding, it's for breaking God's commandments and our sentence is not a fine or a few days in jail, but an eternity in hell, forever out of relationship with God."

"Exactly!" Nick exclaimed, excited that Jen seemed to be getting it now that we were all once again fully engaged and Ferrell-free. "God is totally loving and totally just. Because he is loving and just, the only solution was that

Jesus would die in our place for our sin. Because Jesus was a man he could die for other humans. Because he was God that payment for sin was infinite!"

"I don't know, Nick. It's a good story, but it all sounds unbelievable and, to be honest, too good to be true. It really can't be that simple. We believe and we are forgiven for everything. It's got to be harder than that," Jen observed, but her voice quavered and she sounded like she was hoping Nick could convince her it was all true.

Nick responded, "My youth leader said last week in his talk that faith is trusting in a person I've never met, to take me to a place I've never been. How easy is it to trust in Jesus, a person we've never met, to forgive us for all of our sins and take us to heaven, a place we've never been?" Nick answered his own rhetorical question, "It's so easy that a child could do it and a religious leader could choke on it."

"I don't know, Nick," Jen admitted. "You're saying that Jesus is the way to a meaningful life and to heaven and that's fine. But why not Buddha or Mohammed or whoever? I mean Jesus is cool, but so are all these other religions, right?"

"No," Nick responded while reaching for his backpack. He opened it up and reached in to find his Bible. Opening it up, he flipped through several pages until he finally found what he was looking for.

Nick continued, "Jesus said in John 14:6, 'I am *the* way and *the* truth and *the* life. No one comes to the Father except through me.' " Looking up, Nick said something that got my blood boiling. "Jesus claimed a relationship with him was the *only* way to heaven."

"You mean to tell me that all other religions are on the 'highway to hell'?" I asked angrily.

"No. Not all *other* religions...*all* religions are bound for hell. The word 'religion' comes from the Latin word that means 'to bind back'. *All* religions are trying in one way or another to bind themselves back to God through good deeds, sacrifices, baptism, codes, creeds or whatever. All of it falls short.

"True Christianity, I'm talking here about the relationship with God—not the religion— is not about religion at all," Nick explained. "It's recognizing that there is no way to 'bind ourselves back' to God through our 'good deeds' because compared to God's perfection our good deeds are like filthy rags.

"True Christianity," he went on, "is realizing that God bound himself to humanity through his Son Jesus Christ, that Jesus Christ allowed himself to be bound to a cross for our sins, that he was bound up in a tomb and set free from the bonds of death after three days. And that Jesus offers to unbind us forever from the penalty of sin if we simply trust in him alone as our only hope for forgiveness!"

Nick was on a roll so he kept going, flipping through the pages of his Bible again. "Jesus said in John 6:47, 'I tell you the truth, he who believes has everlasting life.' You see, at the end of the day, the gift of forgiveness, of everlasting eternal life, of heaven, of a personal, permanent relationship with God, is not achieved by our good deeds, but received through faith. It's not a matter of trying, but trusting. And once we put our faith and trust in him alone as the free gift of our forgiveness, God himself becomes our heavenly Father forever. He will love us always. He will always be there for us. No matter how we fall—like I often do, or have fallen in the past—he will love us unconditionally. He will hear all of our prayers and hold us tightly through the storms of life."

Silence.

8

But I couldn't keep silent for long. I was steaming as I shouted, "That's BS!" A few customers looked my way in disgust, but I was too outraged to be distracted for long. "How can a God who is supposed to be so loving send people of different religions who happen to reject Jesus to hell? How is that fair?"

Trying to break the tension with a simple illustration, Nick grabbed my empty Venti cup and said, "Okay, a few weeks back in youth group I was part of this skit that kind of illustrates it. If you promise not to cuss at me, I'll share it with you," Nick said with a half smile.

Calming down I said, "Sorry, dude. It's just hard for me to hear this stuff. It seems narrow-minded to think Jesus is the only way to heaven."

To my surprise, Nick agreed. He said, "It does seem narrow-minded. But being open-minded means we must entertain the logical possibility that the only way to heaven could be through Jesus and Jesus alone. If we don't consider the possibility that Jesus could be the only way, we are not really open-minded. Right?"

Jen reminded me that Nick had been part of Brentwood's championship debate team for the last two years and encouraged me just to nod my head yes. I did with a smile. "Okay," I admitted, "being the open-minded and strikingly handsome atheist that I am, I'll consider the possibility that Jesus could be the only way to heaven."

"Just a minute, I need to find what I want to show you...I know it's in here somewhere," Nick shared. Looking through his pack, I could see that there were a few other books in there. I tried to get a glimpse of the titles but couldn't quite see. Finally, he pulled out three wrinkled pieces of paper. As he flattened them out on the table he held up my empty Venti cup and said, "Okay, we're in Starbucks, right?"

"Duhhh," I responded.

"This skit we did for youth group last week was called *Spiritual Starbucks*. Would you mind if I read it to you?" Nick asked.

"Only if you promise to do all the voices yourself," Jen pushed back.

"Okay," Nick agreed. "Here it goes."

Straightening the papers out as much as he could, he sat up and got into his drama mode. Nick was on the debate team and had been in the drama club in past years. He made me laugh. He cleared his throat the way only wannabe actors can and began to read.

BARISTA: Welcome to Spiritual Starbucks, may I take your order?
CUSTOMER 1: Yes, I'd like a triple *Buddha, Mocha Mohammed Latte*, with an extra shot of religion.
BARISTA: Sure, would you like a *Pious Pastry* with that?
CUSTOMER 1: No, I'm good.
BARISTA: How about a *Hari Krishna Cookie*?
CUSTOMER 1: No, I just ate. Just the drink.

BARISTA: Great, that will be your eternal destiny.

CUSTOMER 1: Is that all?

BARISTA: Yeah, we're running a special. And you get your destiny extra hot...hot as Hell actually.

CUSTOMER 1: Awesome. (*Moves over to wait for his drink. CUSTOMER 2 approaches.*)

BARISTA: Welcome to Spiritual Starbucks. How may I help you?

CUSTOMER 2: Yes, um, this is my first time here...so I don't quite know what to order?

BARISTA: Well, we're glad to have you, sir. Would you like a cold drink, like a Frappacino, or something hot, like a latte?

CUSTOMER 2: I guess something cold.

BARRISTA: Great, a Frappacino. What kind of Frap would you like?

CUSTOMER 2: What kind do you have? (*People in line are getting frustrated.*)

BARISTA: Well, we have your *Mohammed Mocha, Wildberry Wiccan*—

BARRISTA 2: *Caramel Cult Frappacino, Quasi Jesus Frap*—

CUSTOMER 2: Why only a *Quasi Jesus?*

BARISTA: Nobody wants him full strength anymore, sir.

CUSTOMER 2: Umm, well, how about a *Mormon Frappacino?* I've heard those are good.

BARISTA: Yeah, sure we have that—

BARISATA 2: Yeah, but it only comes in decaf.

CUSTOMER 2: Ok, do you have chai tea?

BARISTA: Yes, *Tai Chi Chai Tea*.

CUSTOMER 2: Umm... O.K. I'll have a *Quasi Wildberry Wiccan*, with a shot of *Caramel Cult*.

BARISTA: What size?

CUSTOMER 2: What do you mean?

BARISTA: Well, we have Tall, Grande and Venti.

CUSTOMER 2: What does that mean?

BARISTA: We have small, medium and large. Tall, if you only want a little bit of religion in your life, enough to make you spiritual, but not enough to drive you crazy. Grande, if you want to make a full on commitment to the belief system.

CUSTOMER 2: What does that mean?

BARISTA: Well, if you want to go to the church, the mosque, the coven or whatever meeting every week.

CUSTOMER 2: And what about Venti?

BARISTA: Venti is if you want to be a full-on fanatic for your particular religion.

CUSTOMER 2: Since I'm new to this and I may want to change drinks later on, I'll just go for a Tall this time.

BARISTA: Is that all?

CUSTOMER 2: Yes.

BARISTA: No *Pious Pastries* or *Krishna Cookies?*

CUSTOMER 2: Umm... (*Crowd behind him groans loudly.*) No.

BARISTA: O.K. Let's just ring this up here... That will be your soul.

CUSTOMER 2: Great! Didn't have a need for it anyway. (*Moves over to receive his drink. CUSTOMER 3 approaches.*)

BARISTA: Welcome to Spiritual Starbucks, sir. May I take your order?

CUSTOMER 3: Yes, I'd like a Venti *Full Strength Jesus*, please.

BARISTA: Sorry, sir, but we don't serve *Full Strength Jesus* here. You can have a *Quasi Jesus*, with a shot of something else to spice it up.

CUSTOMER 3: No. I just want straight Jesus please... extra hot. (*More groans from the line.*)

BARISTA 2: Sir. (*Whispering.*) Do you know why we don't serve Venti *Full Strength Jesus* here?

CUSTOMER 3: No.

BARISTA: Because quite honestly, it's a mess. Once we served *Full Strength Jesus*, those who ordered it never wanted anything else. Ever. As a matter of fact, once they ordered it, they never were thirsty for anything again. Which means they didn't order again.

Which means it hurt business. As a matter of fact, they started pestering the other customers and trying to get them to go with the Venti *Full Strength Jesus*. Those who like *Full Strength Jesus Lattes* think it is the way, the truth, the life and the drink that will quench their thirst for all time.

CUSTOMER 3: Well, that's how I want him. Straight and full strength.

BARISTA: Well, you came to the wrong place…NEXT!!!

Nick looked up and said, "Fade to black." He took a seated bow while Jen and I mock clapped. I had to admit it was a pretty funny skit and made a strong point. But I had some questions.

"Okay, okay. That was good," I said, "But how do you know that 'Venti Jesus with nothing added' is the only way to heaven? You say that Jesus was God and man. Why couldn't he just have been a man? A good guy? A spiritual teacher? Don't get me wrong, I believe that Jesus existed and did some good things, but where do you get off claiming that he was God?"

Nick went into his meditative state again while Jen jumped in, "Yeah, Jared. That's a great question. But before we get too much farther into this deal, how much time do we still have before we need to leave?"

I told Jen that we still had twenty minutes before we needed to hit the road.

9

Looking back up, Nick was reengaged once again and said, "There are only a few options for who Jesus really could be."

"What do you mean?" I asked.

"C.S. Lewis, the guy who wrote *The Chronicles of Narnia*, was also a Christian philosopher. He said that there were really only three options for Jesus. He is either Lord, lunatic or a liar."

Jen countered, "That seems a little extreme. Why couldn't he just be, as Jared said, a spiritual leader and teacher?"

"Because Jesus claimed to be God again and again throughout the gospels."

Jen got a confused look on her face, so Nick explained, "The gospels are the first four books of the New Testament that tell the story of the birth, life, ministry, death and resurrection of Jesus from four different perspectives."

"Thanks, Nick," Jen responded, "you may continue."

"Oh may I?" he said with a laugh while flipping his Bible open to the gospels. He showed us a verse where Jesus claimed, in one way or another, to be God. Nick read aloud:

"I give them eternal life, and they shall never perish; no one can snatch them out of my hand. My Father, who has given them to me, is greater than all; no one can snatch them out of my Father's hand. I and the Father are one." Again the Jews picked up stones to stone him, but Jesus said to them, "I have shown you many great miracles from the Father. For which of these do you stone me?" "We are not stoning you for any of these," replied the Jews, "but for blasphemy, because you, a mere man, claim to be God."

Looking up, he added, "That was from John 10, verses 28 through 33."

I admitted, "Those are some pretty hard statements to argue against. If the gospels were accurate, then it does look like Jesus claimed to be God himself."

Jen interrupted, "Dumb blond moment here. I still don't get how him claiming to be God gives us only three options for who he could be: Lord, lunatic or liar."

I answered before Nick could. "Because if he claimed to be God and wasn't, then there are only two possibilities—he was a deluded, crazy, whacked-out nut job or he was lying to everybody."

Nick responded, "Hey, that's pretty good, Jared. Maybe you should join the debate team."

I shot back, "And hang out with all the nerds?"

Jen observed, "You're hanging out with one right now!"

Another tension-breaking moment ensued.

Jen asked, "Okay Nick, that all makes sense. But doesn't that scare you a bit? I mean if Jesus wasn't God, then he was either insane or evil."

Another pondering moment for our good friend. This one took even longer than expected.

Finally, looking up Nick answered, "If Jesus was insane, then how could he speak such a radical message about God's love that would change the course of human history? How could he have shared so many powerful messages of truth that would improve society, relationships and bring hope? How could a nut job have made such a big difference for world history on every level?

"And if he was a liar, don't you think his disciples would have caught on after three years of being with him day and night? Don't you think the religious leaders who hated him would have found out and used these lies against him?"

"Yeah, I guess so." Jen had a look on her face that made me think she was starting to understand where Nick was coming from. "But how do you know, how do you really know that he was God?"

"Because he rose from the dead...and if he did rise from the dead, then he was who he claimed to be."

"Right," we agreed.

Looking down for more than a few seconds Nick shot back up and started going strong again. "Well," he began, "a couple weeks ago at the Easter service, my pastor talked about exactly that issue. First off, he said that it's important to know that the Romans were experts at killing. Around the same time that Jesus was killed, they crucified something like 6,000 people in one day. They knew what it took to kill somebody. They knew when somebody was dead. They made sure that Jesus was dead when he was hanging on the cross by sticking a spear into his rib cage and watching the blood and water flow out, confirming that they'd ruptured the fluid sack that surrounded his heart."

"So Jesus was dead. What's your point?" I pushed.

Long pause, as he looked down and reengaged once again. These long spaces in between our conversation were starting to get ridiculous.

Finally Nick continued, "He was dead and buried, not the typical kind of burial we're familiar with. He was mummified and entombed in a cave and 'locked in' by a huge stone that was rolled over the entrance. Well-trained Roman soldiers were dispatched to guard the tomb to make sure that nobody tried to steal the body and claim 'He is risen!' Three days later, the Bible says, he rose physically from the grave. The soldiers passed out they were so afraid at what was going on. Over the next forty days he appeared to over 500 witnesses. These witnesses claimed to have seen him first-hand."

"So what?" I challenged, "They could have just been saying that they saw the resurrected Jesus. They could have been making it up!"

"Yes, they could have. But that's not likely," Nick replied. "Many of these witnesses were tortured and murdered for their claim that they had seen the risen Jesus. Now, as someone has said, some people will die for what they think to be the truth, but nobody will die for what they know to be a lie."

"I don't mean to hurt your feelings, Nick," Jen shared, "but I think this all sounds farfetched."

"Me too," I agreed.

"Well, then both of you have a gigantic task in front of you," Nick declared.

"What?" we asked in unison.

"You have to find a better explanation for how we got here, what life is all about, why there's evil in the world, what redemption looks like and means, why we feel guilty about some things and what happens after we die. The story of Christianity answers all these questions and more. So what's your explanation for all of it?"

10

I jumped in headfirst and stated flatly, "I've already told you mine. I don't believe in God."

"That's not telling me your explanation. That's just telling me what you don't believe. What do you believe?" Nick pushed.

I pushed back, "I believe we are the result of evolution. That we live, that we die and that's basically it."

Nick perked up, "So then why do you feel guilty when you do something wrong?"

"I don't see how that has anything to do with—" I stopped myself mid-sentence, paused for a moment and thought out loud, "I guess I've always assumed that our ideas of right and wrong come from our parents...and that it all has something to do with what's in the common good for the survival of the species."

"Or maybe," Nick came back, "God created us with a conscience. Maybe he gave us this conscience to help us determine right from wrong. Maybe he created us with the capacity to feel these guilty feelings as an inner reminder that he is there, he is watching and that someday we will give an account to him for everything we've ever done wrong."

It was a 'holy crap' moment...for a moment. If Nick was right, then I was in trouble. Thank God Nick turned his gaze off of me for a second.

Turning to Jen, Nick asked, "And what's your explanation for all this, Jen?"

"Ummmm...," Jen admitted, "I guess I don't know. I just figure that I'll find out when I die."

I jumped back in. "But if what Nick is saying is true, then when you die it will be too late. You'll be burning in the flames of hell, getting

poked and prodded by the devil's pitchfork.
Right, Nick?"

"Something like that," Nick agreed. I could
tell he wasn't quite sure whether to smile at
what I had intended to be a joke.

Just then I remembered that I'd forgotten
to tell my mom and dad that I wasn't coming
home for dinner. That's all I needed, another
lecture from dad about responsibility and
communication and blah, blah, blah. Reaching
for my phone, I realized that it was out of juice.
My mom and dad had probably been trying
to call me. There were probably ten messages
asking me where I was.

"Hey, Nick, can I borrow your phone?" I
asked.

"Sure," he answered, bringing it up from
under the table. A strange look came across
Nick's face as he hesitantly handed it to me.
His facial expression struck me as odd, but I
didn't think much about it. I was too worried
about getting in trouble with my parents. Just
as I was about to dial home, I noticed a text
come up on Nick's phone. "Oh, you got a text
message. Let me check it for you," I said half
joking, while opening it with my thumb.

"NO!!!" Nick jumped to his feet with a shockingly loud yell that startled the other customers, not to mention Jen and me.

Nick was hiding something, and as I looked down at the text it became obvious what he was hiding. The text message simply read: *Ask thm wht hppns 2 a soul aftr deth n thr wrld view.*

I started laughing like a crazy man.

"What?" Jen wanted to know what was up, as Nick fell back in his chair, looking like a three year old caught with his hand in the cookie jar.

"Our little Christian friend here has been cheating," I laughed, but underneath the laugh, I was a little steamed. Then with a sudden burst of insight I exclaimed, "And we were thinking that every time your head went down you were praying or meditating or something. Here we thought that you were probably the smartest person on the planet by knowing all this stuff and you're getting fed answers by—who's texting you, man?" I asked.

"My youth leader," Nick said with all the blood drained from his already pale face. He continued his confession while Jen and I just laughed and laughed. "When I first went into the bathroom I called him and asked him what I should do and he suggested that I text him quick questions and he would text me back quick answers and questions to ask you. He's really smart about all this stuff and I knew he'd have some of these answers. He talks about this stuff all the time in youth group."

Jen was still laughing when she asked, "So you didn't really have to go to the bathroom? You were just getting argument ammo from your youth leader?"

"No. I really had to go. But while I was in there I called him, both times."

"Ewww. Once again, thanks for the graphic description," Jen sarcastically scolded him.

"I'm really sorry, guys," Nick went on. "I guess you could say that's one of my weaknesses—I don't like to look stupid in front of my friends."

While we were talking, I was scrolling through the text chain of questions and answers on Nick's phone. His youth leader was definitely feeding him answers, but not all the answers. Nick knew enough on his own to stand his ground. Or at least I thought he did.

"Okay, since we're confessing our sins here, I've got a question for you, Nick," I said. "What's in the backpack?"

Nick reached in and grabbed two books. One was called *More Than a Carpenter* and the other was called *A Case for Christ*. I'd never heard of either. He threw the books on the table with an I've-been-caught-again look of embarrassment.

Jen grabbed one and I grabbed the other and we started flipping through these books. They were well-worn, underlined and had things written in the margins. While we were looking through these books Nick explained that both of these authors, Josh Mcsomething and Lee Stobel, or Storbell, or whatever, were both at one time skeptics themselves who were convinced of the faith as they had taken on the challenge of examining the evidence for Jesus being the Son of God.

"Were you reading these in the bathroom, too?" Jen asked.

"Yes," Nick admitted.

"Gross!" she said as she threw her book back down on the table.

"Why are they so marked up?" I asked.

Nick's answer surprised me. He said, "I've been studying them for three months trying to get ready for this conversation."

"What do you mean?" Jen asked.

"I've been praying for the last year for a conversation like this to happen with you and Jen...and Kailey. I know that after we graduate, we'll all be going our separate ways and I wanted to tell you guys about Jesus before it was too late."

"I know you've tried to bring it up with me several times, and I shut you down every time," I admitted.

I couldn't help but be a little flattered by Nick's heartfelt efforts. Jen expressed my sentiments when she asked, "So you've been studying all these facts and statistics because you don't want to see us go to hell?"

"Right," Nick said, girding himself for a follow up zinger.

11

But no zinger came. To be honest, this whole conversation hadn't been as bad as I'd thought it would be. In fact, now that I thought about it, Nick was just laying it out there for us. We had a real friend who truly believed that if we didn't trust in Jesus or whatever, that we'd end up in hell. The fact that he had been praying for an opportunity for a year and studying for a conversation like it was some final exam impressed me. I'm not kidding. It really did.

"I'm sorry that I deceived you guys. Will you forgive me?" Nick asked. I was a little surprised by how serious his apology sounded. "I should have just been straight up with you that I wasn't quite ready yet for all your questions. I should have just said 'I don't know', instead of sneaking text message answers from my youth leader."

"Of course we forgive you, Nick!" Jen said for the both of us. "Personally, I think it's kind of sweet that you care so much about us that you were willing to do anything to get us the right answers."

Nick continued, "Well, speaking of the 'right answers', I've got something else to admit to you."

"What this time," I joked. "Did you sneak Jesus pills into our lattes when we weren't looking?"

He smiled and said, "No, no. It's just that I've not told you the real reason that I became a Christian, and it wasn't any of the facts that I just shared with you. As a matter of fact, I hadn't even heard any of this stuff before I became a Christian. It was years later that I discovered all this awesome evidence of the Christian faith."

"So what got you to believe Christianity was true?" Jen asked, her curiosity fully peaked.

I wanted to know too. I knew that Nick didn't come from a religious background. Nick's mom was definitely not the church-going type.

"Well, like you already know, I've never met my real father. But I don't think I've ever given you the full picture of how bad things were for me when I was a kid. You see, Mom has been married three times, but none of her marriages have lasted longer than a couple years. Most of the guys she married were jerks. One guy named Paul used to beat me up when he got drunk. I remember as a kid wondering what life was all about. I even thought about suicide. I mean, I was ten years old and was already thinking about blowing my brains out. Can you believe that?"

"No," I stated flatly, shocked at what I was hearing.

Nick continued, "In fifth grade this kid, Jeremy, transferred into my elementary school mid year. He and I became friends right off. There was something about him I really liked."

In my mind, I knew exactly what Nick was talking about. It's the same reason that I had so easily connected with him back when we were freshmen. But I wasn't going to tell him that.

Nick went on with his story. "One day we were skateboarding and he just started talking to me about God. To be honest, I had never thought much about God or anything like that. But it caught my attention.

"I ended up going to church with him and his family on Easter. The preacher was talking about God in a way that really had me interested. He talked about God as a Father in heaven who longs to have a relationship with us, who loved us so much that he sent his own Son to earth to be sacrificed for our sins—so that we could be in relationship with him. I remember getting a strange feeling in my gut when the preacher shared that Jesus rose from the dead and how that was the real meaning of Easter. I thought that if this story was true it was the greatest thing in the world."

"Why did you think it was so great?" Jen asked.

"Because I knew that if it was true, somebody really loved me. They loved me enough to die for me." Nick's voice quavered a little as he answered Jen.

Before I could stop the words from coming out of my mouth I blurted, "So what did you do, Nick?" He looked at me and said, "Right there in church, I asked God to be my Dad, and I put my trust in Jesus to save me from my sins and to give me hope."

Nick paused for a moment, but both Jen and I were quiet so he continued, "On the way home, I told Jeremy's family what I'd done and his mom gave me a gospel of John to read. I read the whole thing from cover to cover that night before I went to bed."

"Whoaaa, that's pretty cool," Jen added, her eyes slowly starting to well up.

Nick continued, "Yeah. I didn't know any of the facts about who created the world, or whether it evolved, or anything about Jesus rising from the dead or whatever. All I knew is that I was a sinner, that I deserved hell, that Jesus died for me and that God loved me. That night I literally cried myself to sleep knowing for the first time that I had a daddy that loved me no matter what. I had a daddy that would never beat me, would never leave me, would never condemn me. I had a daddy, a heavenly father who loved me so much that he sacrificed his only son that I could be his son. That's why I became a Christian, guys."

I was getting nervous. I was thinking thoughts and feeling feelings I had never had before. I was seriously wondering if there was a God—and if that God could love someone like me.

But Nick wasn't done, and to be honest I was glad because, at that point, I was afraid of talking for fear of going into emotional overload. "You guys are always telling me that you see something in me that's different. What you see is not me—it's Jesus in me. He is my hope, my joy and he alone satisfies the deep longings of my soul like nothing else can.

"Jen, you are always asking me why I don't go partying with you on the weekends. It's not because I'm above it. I'm not. I guess you could say that I've ordered a Venti *Full Strength Jesus*, and it's because Jesus is on the inside of my soul, the only thing that makes me truly happy is making him happy."

"Dude, you always seem so happy, no matter what," I added.

"Don't get me wrong, Jared. I've got problems like everyone else. You know how devastated I was when I got dumped by Brittany last year. Did it hurt? Yes. What got me through? Jesus. What's getting me through now that I can't get an athletic scholarship after I messed up my knee and had to drop out of track? Jesus. What's going to get me through now that I'm going to have to work my way through college? Jesus. What will get me through whatever may come my way? Jesus.

"I know you may think of Jesus as a crutch for me. He's not. I know this may sound weird, but he is my stretcher. He's my everything. He makes my life worth living. It's not the facts of creation versus evolution, not the Lord, lunatic, liar stuff that gives me hope—it's Jesus himself. All those facts and stuff give me mental confidence that my Christian faith is on firm footing, but it's Jesus that meets the deepest needs of my soul. It was Jesus that convinced me that he was real, not human arguments. He came into my life and changed everything."

12

Jen had been listening intently up to that moment and then her face clouded and the tears started to slip out.

Deep down, I knew why. She'd spilled her guts often enough about the battles that raged at home between her alcoholic dad and her religious rules mom. About how she couldn't wait to graduate and get out of the house. I knew she was emotionally out there on her own, distant from both her parents, and like I said earlier, she'd been looking for love in all the wrong places for awhile now.

"For years I've been looking for ways to escape all the crap at home," Jen said as the tears slid down her face. "Escaping the pain—that's really what all the partying and sex are about. But that stuff hasn't changed anything...in fact, in some ways it's just made things worse. I always walk away feeling used and empty, and feeling like, what's the point. And guilty, sometimes I just feel like everything wrong in my life is so my fault—" She buried her face in her hands and just sat there sobbing.

Nick shifted over to the empty chair next to her.

"I, I—" she struggled to get control and push the words out.

Between the tears she began to choke out the words. "I need—something. I need—a—a—a daddy. I need—forgive—forgiveness."

And now for the most awkward moment of my entire life, right there in our favorite Starbucks in front of complete strangers, Jen told Nick that she was ready to become a Christian. I guess you could say she was, according to the little skit, ordering a Venti *Full Strength Jesus* for the first time.

It was weird and moving at the same time. It was so weird that I think if the customers who were there earlier hadn't left, the manager would have asked us to go outside.

Jen was crying. Nick was crying. And before I knew it, I was feeling a little emotional myself. It wasn't because I wanted to become a Christian right then and there like Jen. It's because for the first time, I viewed Christianity as something different than some rule-riddled religion. I saw it as a beautiful story that, if true, was the greatest thing in the history of mankind.

Nick told Jen that saying a prayer to God wouldn't plunge her into a relationship with Jesus. He told her that only trusting in Jesus to forgive her sins would. He shared with her that saying a prayer to God was a way to let God know that today she became his child. He asked her if she understood. She said yes.

"Can I lead you through a prayer to God?" Nick asked.

"Yes," Jen said, still sniffling.

"Now saying a prayer doesn't make you a Christian. It's just a way to let God know that you are accepting the free gift of his love," Nick emphasized.

Jen nodded silently.

"Repeat these words after me," Nick said softly. "Dear God—"

"Dear God—" she repeated.

"I know that I've messed up."

Starting to cry again, she whispered, "I know that I've messed up."

"I know that I could never be good enough to get into your perfect heaven."

She wiped her cheek with the back of her hand and said, "I know that I could never be good enough to get into your perfect heaven."

"But right now I believe that Jesus died for all my sins and rose from the dead three days later." Nick prayed.

She repeated these words with more confidence. I could tell she was really talking to God.

Nick continued, "And I trust him alone as my only hope of forgiveness right now."

She repeated.

Nick wrapped it up, "Thank you for making me your child."

She lost it again, but finally was able to choke out the words.

When they both looked up, they immediately embraced and before I could stop myself, I joined in. Here we were in a group hug in the middle of Starbucks, their tears flowing and my mind still racing.

As we got up to leave, Nick invited both of us to come with him to his next youth group meeting, since they were going to be talking about the reliability of the Bible or something. Youth group didn't sound quite as Amish to me this time.

Then Nick reached into his backpack one more time and pulled out two small, identical, paperback books. Gospels of John, he called them. He explained that it was the one book of the Bible that was written to people who didn't believe in Jesus. He asked us both if we would read it later that night, after we watched *Grease* together. We both said yes.

So much for the after party...I told you my plans were going to be ruined.

Actually though, I'm looking forward to it. I can party anytime—and usually do—but there's something intriguing about this God stuff. Maybe there's something to it.

Maybe.

If you can't tell, I'm not yet fully convinced. But I'm definitely in a different place than I was an hour ago.

Nick told us he wasn't going to push us to buy into it. He didn't. He painted a picture, though. His perspective was interesting to hear and debate about. I don't know for sure if I buy all his '*facts*'—or his text messaging youth leader's facts, for that matter. But it's the message of Jesus himself that's got me thinking on a whole different level.

I wonder what Sandra D is going to think about all this.

Speaking of Kailey—we gotta go. It's almost show time!

» If you'd like to read the gospel of John, go to www.dare2share.org/ventijesus.

» If you want to read about more of the facts that support Christianity, check out *More Than a Carpenter* by Josh McDowell or *A Case for Christ* and *A Case for a Creator* by Lee Strobel.

» If you want to order more *Venti Jesus Please* books to pass along to your friends, go to www.dare2share.org/ventijesus.

» To download a video presentation of the gospel to your iPod or myspace page, go to www.gospeljourney.com.

Greg Stier is the President of Dare 2 Share and has equipped teenagers across the United States to share Jesus with their friends with courage, clarity and compassion. He, his wife Debbie, and their two children, Jeremy and Kailey live in Arvada, Colorado. For more information check out his blog at www.gregstier.org.